CONTENTS

swoosh!

PEANUT BUTTER AND JELLY

BEN CLANTON

Farshore

FOR ALEX COX!
KEEP SPREADING THE AWESOMENESS!

Farshore

FIRST PUBLISHED IN CANADA 2018 BY TUNDRA BOOKS

FIRST PUBLISHED IN GREAT BRITAIN IN 2019 BY FARSHORE

AN IMPRINT OF HARPERCOLLINS*PUBLISHERS*
1 LONDON BRIDGE STREET, LONDON SE1 9GF

FARSHORE.CO.UK

HARPERCOLLINS*PUBLISHERS*
1ST FLOOR, WATERMARQUE BUILDING,
RINGSEND ROAD, DUBLIN 4, IRELAND

TEXT AND ILLUSTRATIONS COPYRIGHT © 2018 BEN CLANTON

ISBN 978 1 4052 9532 1
PRINTED IN ITALY
4

A CIP CATALOGUE RECORD FOR THIS TITLE IS AVAILABLE FROM THE BRITISH LIBRARY

MIX
Paper from
responsible sources
FSC™ C007454

FSC
www.fsc.org

This book is produced from independently certified FSC™ paper
to ensure responsible forest management.

For more information visit: www.harpercollins.co.uk/green

A SWEET
AND SALTY
STORY!

AHOY, JELLY!
WHAT IS THAT SMALL, STRANGE WAFFLE YOU'RE EATING?
nom nom nom

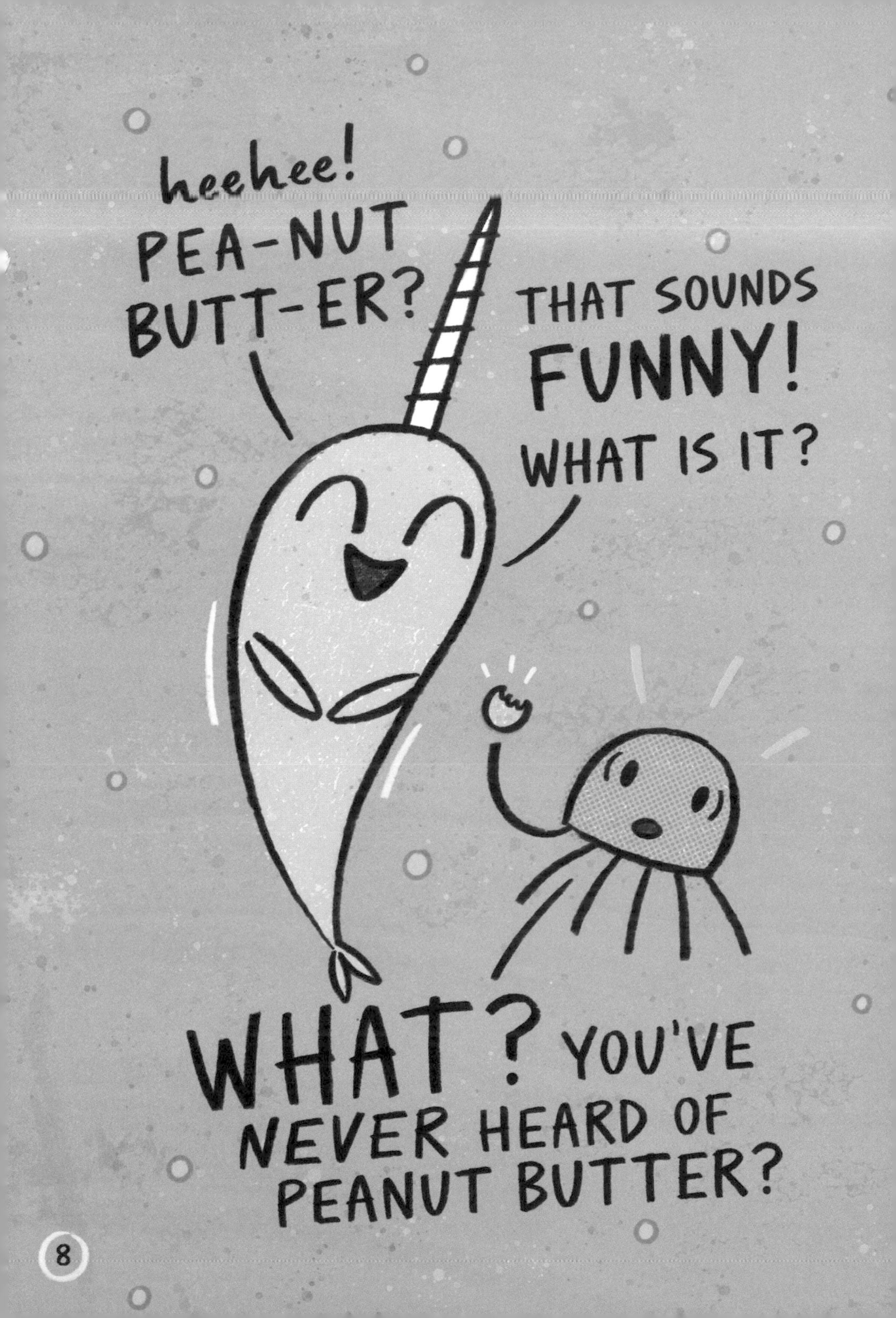
heehee!
PEA-NUT BUTT-ER?
THAT SOUNDS FUNNY!
WHAT IS IT?
WHAT? YOU'VE NEVER HEARD OF PEANUT BUTTER?

YUCK!

HAVE YOU
ACTUALLY
EATEN
SOMETHING
LIKE THAT
BEFORE?

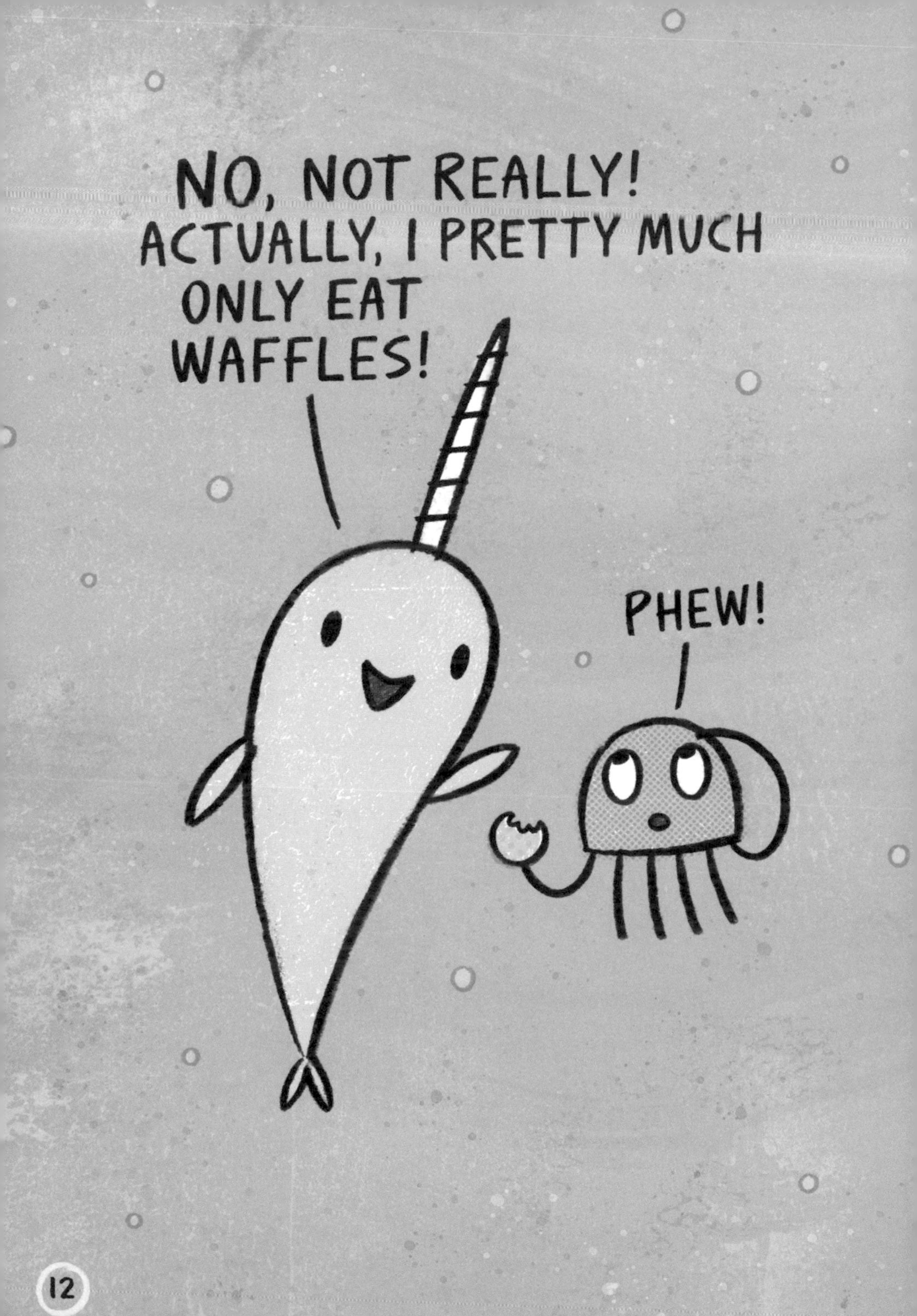
NO, NOT REALLY! ACTUALLY, I PRETTY MUCH ONLY EAT WAFFLES!
PHEW!

WAIT A MINUTE...
ONLY WAFFLES?

CAKE? APPLES?
CHEESE? PIE?
ARTICHOKES?
MARSHMALLOWS?
GUACAMOLE?
UH...SUSHI?
FRENCH FRIES?

19

WHY?

HAVE YOU EVER HEARD OF "TOO MUCH OF A GOOD THING"?

THAT'S SILLY! HOW CAN YOU HAVE TOO MANY WAFFLES?

RIGHT... NEVER MIND.

BUT MAYBE YOU'LL LIKE THIS COOKIE EVEN MORE THAN WAFFLES!

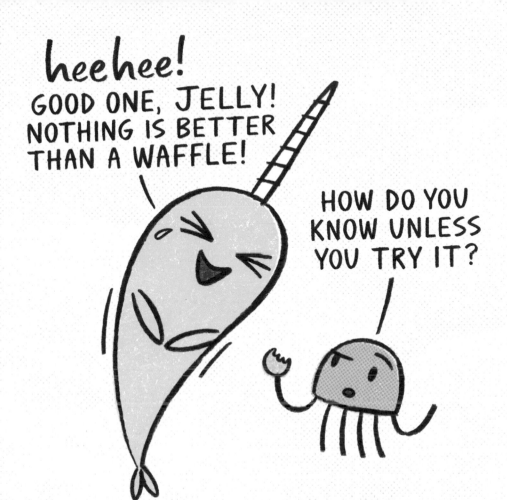

I TELL YOU WHAT,
I'LL MAKE YOU AN
EXTRA LARGE
WAFFLE IF YOU JUST
TRY THIS PEANUT
BUTTER COOKIE.

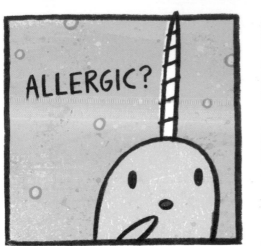

*THE ALLERGIC AQUATIC ANIMALS AWARENESS ASSOCIATION
ADVISES CAUTION WHEN TRYING A COMMON ALLERGEN.

IT'S FIN TASTIC!

DELICIOUS FACTS

SCIENTISTS BELIEVE NARWHALS SUCK UP THEIR FOOD WHOLE AND EAT MAINLY FISH.

I PREFER WAFFLES!

AND PEANUT BUTTER!

MOST JELLYFISH STING THEIR PREY WITH THEIR TENTACLES BEFORE EATING IT.

BLUE WHALES (THE LARGEST ANIMAL EVER) EAT MAINLY TINY LITTLE KRILL. THEY EAT OODLES OF THEM. AS MANY AS 40 MILLION KRILL PER DAY!

YUM!

EEK!

HUMPBACK WHALES WORK TOGETHER TO CREATE COMPLEX BUBBLE NETS TO CORRAL FISH TO EAT.

SEA CUCUMBERS EAT ALL SORTS OF THINGS, INCLUDING POOP.

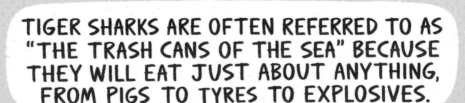

TIGER SHARKS ARE OFTEN REFERRED TO AS "THE TRASH CANS OF THE SEA" BECAUSE THEY WILL EAT JUST ABOUT ANYTHING, FROM PIGS TO TYRES TO EXPLOSIVES.

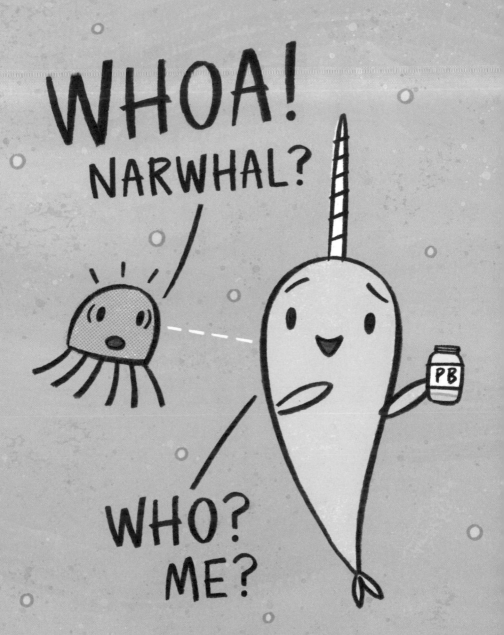

YES, YOU! NARWHAL, WHAT HAPPENED? YOU'RE ALL—

OH, MY NAME ISN'T NARWHAL. MY NAME IS PEANUT BUTTER.

PEANUT BUTTER? THAT IS **NOT** A NAME!

IT IS NOW! I USED TO GO BY NARWHAL, BUT...

...I LOVE PEANUT BUTTER SO MUCH I DECIDED TO CHANGE MY NAME. SEE!

AHOY! MY NAME IS
PEANUT BUTTER

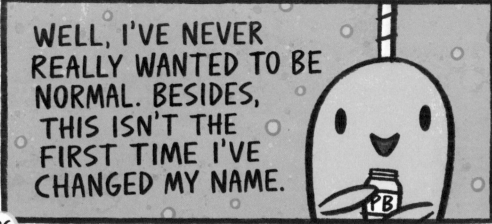

AND BEFORE THAT I WAS NAUTILUS III. OH, AND I WAS CALLED JAMIE FOR A WHILE... AND I OFTEN LIKE TO GO BY SIR DUCKWORTH. CHANGING NAMES IS FUN!

UGH! LOOK, PEANUT BUTTER OR **NARWHAL** OR **FRED** OR WHATEVER YOU ARE CALLING YOURSELF... DON'T YOU THINK YOU'RE TAKING THIS PEANUT BUTTER THING A BIT TOO FAR?

FLOYD...

SUPER WAFFLE
AND STRAWBERRY SIDEKICK
VS PB&J

Peanut Butter   Floyd

by ~~Narwhal~~ and ~~Jelly~~

SUPER WAFFLE AND STRAWBERRY SIDEKICK HAVE BEATEN ANGRY ROBOTS AND VILLAINOUS BLOBS, SO THIS DILL PICKLE WILL BE A PIECE OF CAKE ...PIECE OF PICKLE?

47

PEANUT

A.K.A. mini
NARWHAL

 NOW THAT I AM SUPER SMALL ALL THE WAFFLES WILL SEEM **HUGE** TO ME!

 I CAN EAT **GIANT** WAFFLES!

 OH.

 GOOD POINT!

THE NEXT DAY...

. . . NOW THAT I'M **ENORMOUS** I CAN EAT OODLES OF WAFFLES! I'LL BREAK THE **WORLD RECORD** FOR WAFFLE EATING!

THAT IS . . . INGENIOUS!